Jack's Tracks

Story by

C. J. Livingstone

– To J & K and model train enthusiasts everywhere

For Jack's seventh birthday, he got pencils and socks,
And something wrapped up in a rectangular box.
A train, a controller, and eight pieces of track,
Three little coaches, and a power pack.

He clicked them together and, admiring the scale,
Placed the engine and wagons carefully onto the rails.
The train went around for a couple of times,
Then Jack exclaimed loudly, "We need more lines!"

He felt the desire to expand his creation,
To add signals, a turnout, and maybe a station.
"Dad, I need more! We have to grow bigger."
"This railroad's not done!" he declared, full of vigor.

So reluctantly, Dad handed over his cash.
Jack took off to the store at a double-fast dash.
Browsing the aisles, he filled up his cart
And headed right back to his bedroom to start.

He added the new to the original set.
It was certainly better, but he wasn't done yet.
As he shunted the engines and coaches unfettered,
He thought very carefully about what could be bettered.

He surveyed the whole railroad but was not satisfied.
"I need scenery, like rivers and mountains," he cried.
So he went to the library and scoured the books,
And that's when he discovered *Great Modeling Looks*.

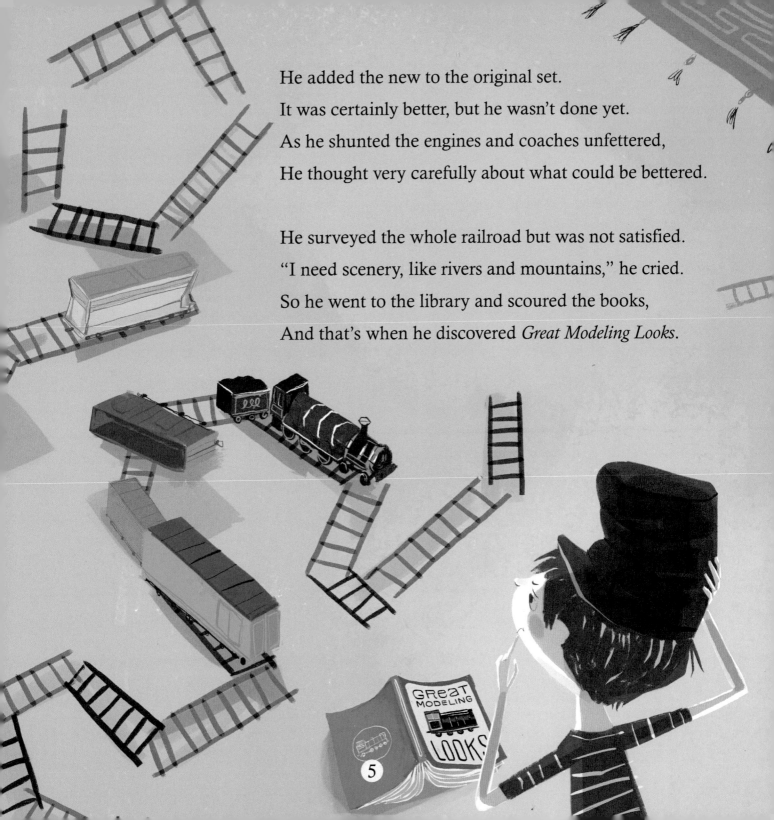

GReaT
MODELING
LOOKS

He devoted himself to study that day,
To learn railroad modeling the professional way.
Carpentry, electrics, paint, and construction,
And the intricate details of scenery production.

And when he was done, he had made a great plan,
Then he sketched out a map of this miniature land.
But what's more, he had all of the requisite skills
To tackle this tricky and challenging build.

He went to his father to unveil the design
And said, "Dad, I need money for all the supplies,
To build airports, harbors, tunnels and such."
But Dad said, "No, Son, this is getting too much."

But from this small setback, Jack was not deterred.
To find a solution, he was in fact stirred.
So he searched through the
classifieds for almost a day
Until he found an old gent
who was moving away.

Jack told him his plans over three cups of tea.

Then the old fellow said, "You can have mine for free.

I don't really need it, and I see that you're taken

With a grand old idea, so get fabricatin'."

So they lugged that old railway set back to the house.

Though his parents were quiet, they did have their doubts.

But Jack set to work without any delay,

And he hammered and soldered and painted all day.

8

In the early afternoon came a knock at the door.

It was one of the neighborhood kids, name of Paul.

"I saw you," he said, "with some pretty cool gear, and

I'd be happy to help. If you needed a hand."

"Sure," said Jack, as he weathered a reefer.

"You can start out by painting this old western steamer."

So Paul took his paint brush straight to a funnel.

And as for their output, it instantly doubled.

Then more kids came over when the news got around
That Jack was building a miniature town.
They were inspired by his limitless drive for construction,
And they wanted to help, so they asked for instruction.

He put them to work making Paris of plaster,

And if they dallied at all, then he made them go faster.

They emptied their piggy banks and bought track by the yard,

So the railroad could grow exponentially large.

Now the speed they were working demanded they find
Building materials of all different kinds.
When the money ran out, they had to use smarts,
So they foraged all over the town for spare parts.

They found an old clubhouse with junk in the back,
And they loaded their wagons with supplies for the track.
They took all the stuff that was wanted no more
And made mountains from sofas and fields from a door.

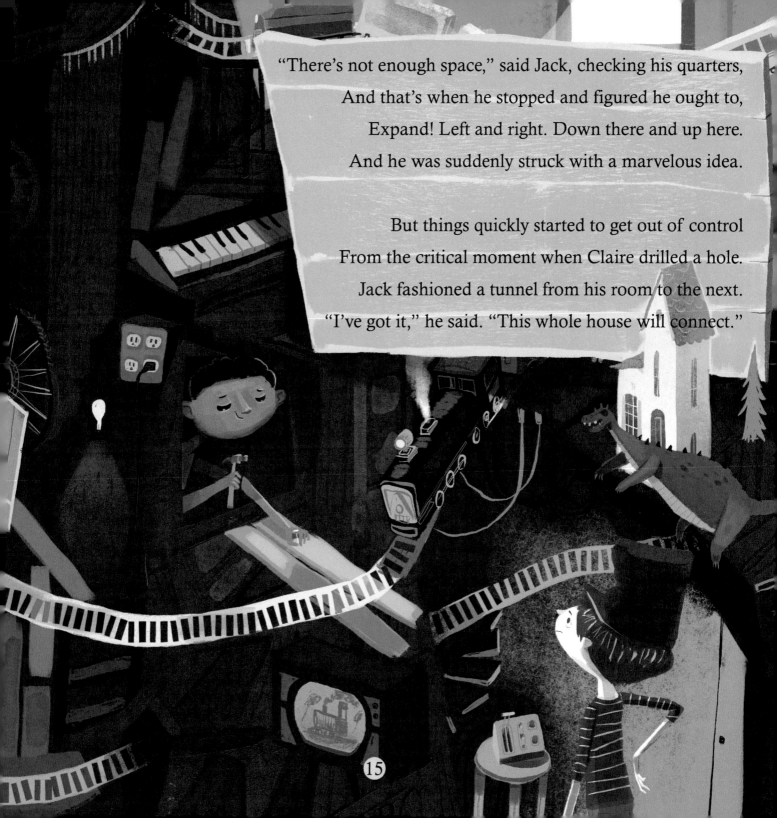

"There's not enough space," said Jack, checking his quarters,
And that's when he stopped and figured he ought to,
Expand! Left and right. Down there and up here.
And he was suddenly struck with a marvelous idea.

But things quickly started to get out of control
From the critical moment when Claire drilled a hole.
Jack fashioned a tunnel from his room to the next.
"I've got it," he said. "This whole house will connect."

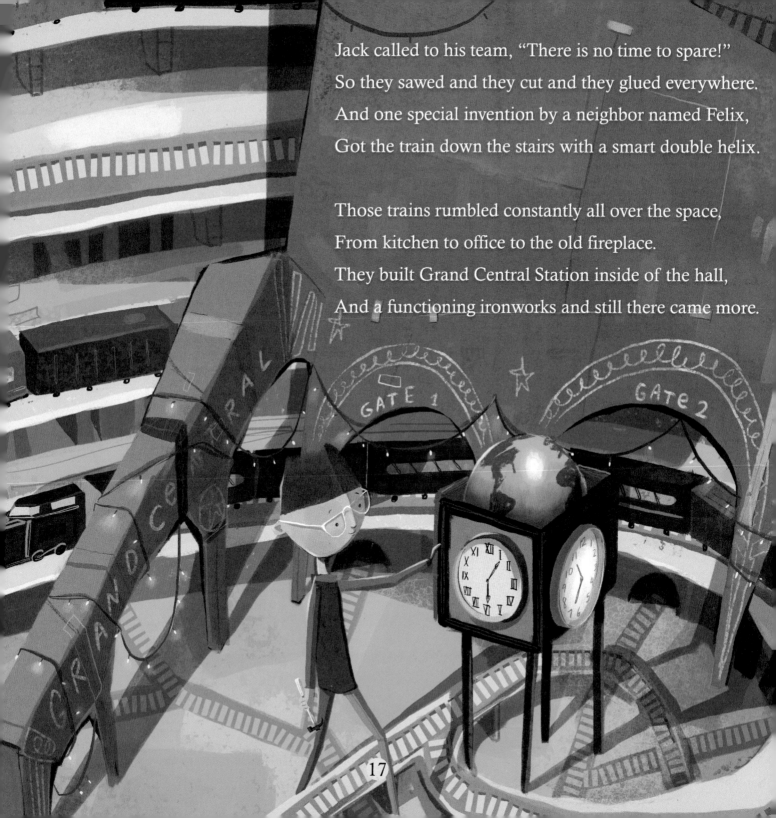

Jack called to his team, "There is no time to spare!"
So they sawed and they cut and they glued everywhere.
And one special invention by a neighbor named Felix,
Got the train down the stairs with a smart double helix.

Those trains rumbled constantly all over the space,
From kitchen to office to the old fireplace.
They built Grand Central Station inside of the hall,
And a functioning ironworks and still there came more.

17

Now Jack became king of all he surveyed,

A captain of industry, above and at grade.

He had diesels and locos that left day and night,

And the neighborhood kids all watched with delight.

Down to the port came the coal from the quarry,

And along by the ships ran the local bus-trolley.

A high-speed train whizzed from city to city

While the branch line putted through valleys so pretty.

Now every aspect of home life from breakfast to cradle
Was governed by a long and complex timetable.
And Jack's parents, who up to this point were quite calm,
Started to feel a sense of alarm.

"There's too much. We can't live," they started to say,
But Jack's team kept on building day after day.
Until one afternoon, when enough was enough,
And his mother declared, "Jack! Get rid of this stuff!"

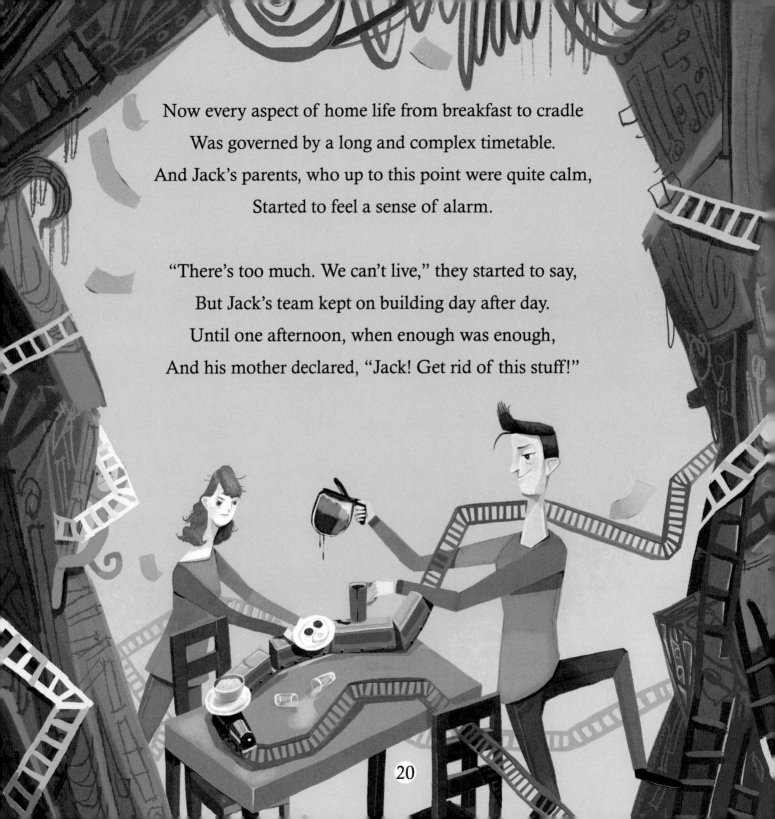

"I won't do it!" called Jack, stomping back to his room,

And he locked the door and refused to resume

His school work until they had settled the issue.

So there he remained, making clouds out of tissue.

Nobody saw him. It caused them distress.

His mom sent him dinner on the 5.30 express,

But the food didn't work, and he sent it right back

On an old diesel switcher carrying dirty coal sacks.

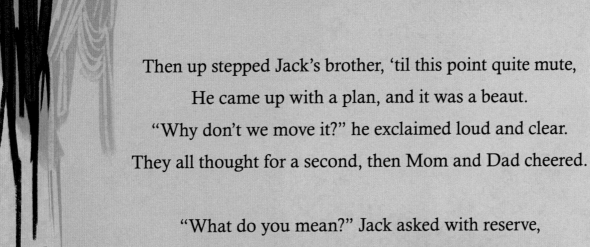

Then up stepped Jack's brother, 'til this point quite mute,

He came up with a plan, and it was a beaut.

"Why don't we move it?" he exclaimed loud and clear.

They all thought for a second, then Mom and Dad cheered.

"What do you mean?" Jack asked with reserve,

Sensing his interests were not very well served.

Said Brother, "Take it down. Put it somewhere that's new.

With the help of our friends, we could accomplish it too!"

"But where would it go?" pondered Jack with concern.
And his brother thought long on each option in turn.
Then he picked up the phone and called the town's mayor,
"Put me on to his highness. I wish to confer."

Now Keaton, for that was Jack's brother's first name,
Went to the Mayor of their town the next day.
He sat down in his office and, with a short wait,
said, "Mister Mayor, please, let's negotiate."

"That old clubhouse you have, in a state of decay,
The kids want to use it, if you'll give it away."
"Heavens no!" cried the Mayor, without more than a thought,
But Keaton was smarter than a five-year-old ought.

"Please, Mr. Mayor, just stay in your seat,"
And he proceeded to set out his demands in a neat
Presentation that he'd worked on all through the night.
The mayor thought about it, then said, "Oh, alright."

So the day soon arrived when the railroad would move,
And the kids from the neighborhood all got into the groove.
They took every part out, piece by piece,
And walked it with care, to the end of the street.

They put the skills that they learned to very good use,
And they made that old clubhouse look just about new.
With Jack in charge things went exactly as planned,
Supported by Keaton, his next-in-command.

And when it was done, he looked over the place,
And concluded that yes, he was really amazed.
From one single set, a behemoth had grown,
From those eight pieces of track that he'd built on his own.

And the children took turns to control the new system.
One checked the rails, while another would switch 'em.
Still more of them helped those old steamers to run.
Jack thought to himself, "My work here is done."

Now back in his room, just a bed and a chair,
Without all of that track, things looked really quite bare,
And although Jack knew it was in a good place,
That expression of sadness would not leave his face.

Now his dad, walking by, stopped and considered
The remarkable feat that his son had delivered.
He thought, "I must do something to cheer up my boy,"
And decided to buy him a brand spanking new toy.

A slot car set in a neat little box,

A figure of eight with two controllers on top,

They clicked it together and started to race.

Until Keaton said, "Jack, we're going to need more space…"

Made in the USA
Columbia, SC
25 October 2022

69561220R00020